LAKE COMO
Bellagio

MILANO

PARMA

GENOVA
Portofino
Santa Margherita

FIRENZE

CHIANTI

UMBRIA

ROMA

First U.S. edition 2013

ISBN 978-0-9896224-0-0

Library of Congress Control Number. 2013913183

Printed and bound in Malaysia for Imago
www.imagogroup.com

Designed by SUSAK PRESS
www.susakpress.org

Edited by Roberta Butler

Cover lettering by Jim Bunker

Travels with Mac 'n' Row

by
Mackenzie Henson

Assisted by
Row Henson

Meet Mac and Row

My name is Mackenzie, but my friends call me Mac. I'm a twelve-year-old black American Labrador Retriever,🐾[1] and I spend half of the year in the south of France and half of the year in the south of the United States. I guess you can say I'm a southern girl. My U.S. friends, human and animal, speak English. Some of my friends in France speak English too, but most speak French. I understand only a few words of French. Fortunately, we dogs can always find other ways to communicate.

Our friends find our U.S. house by looking for our bright red door, and they find our house in France by looking for its French blue one. In either house, in either country, friends, whether two-legged or four-legged, will be both welcomed and well fed when they visit us.

Of all my friends, my very best friend is my mom, and this book is the story of how we found each other. Her real name is Rowena, but everyone calls her Row. She travels with me. Most of her friends think I'm the luckiest dog in the world, but I've not always been a world traveler. Before I met Row, I had hardly ever been far from the place I was born.

I spent the first two years of my life learning how to hunt ducks. Born at a kennel known for their duck-hunting dogs, I came from a long line of ribbon winners. Like many hunters, my previous owner kept me in the back of his truck or in a pen outside his house. This was the only life I knew, and I was happy — or so I thought.

One day, during his travels, my owner stopped to take an old friend to lunch. Her name was Row. It was a warm day, and when she saw me in the back of his truck, she asked that I be allowed to stay inside her house while they went out for lunch because she was concerned that it would be too hot for me in the truck.

You see, she had long been a dog lover, having had dogs in her life from a very early age, but she had been without a dog for a long time. She had a busy job that required a lot of travel, so she felt it wouldn't be fair to have a dog in her life. That all changed when Row met me.

It was love at first sight. Since my owner traveled much of the time, Row asked if she might keep me on occasion to help him out, and he willingly consented. It didn't take me long to figure out that I belonged with her. Whenever my then-owner would come to pick me up, I would stand behind Row and look up at her with the "please-don't-make-me-leave" look.

II

Don't get me wrong; my owner wasn't mean to me nor did he mistreat me, but I was not destined for a life in the back of a truck. I was destined for a life of world travel and adventure. The only ducks I could see in my future were alive and quacking in the Canal du Midi or swimming on Lake Como. But I'm getting ahead of myself. Those stories will come later in the book.

When my previous owner would come to pick me up, he would coax me to come with him and go back into the crate in the back of his truck. Being the very obedient and well-trained dog that I am, I would go with him — but my heart would stay with Row.

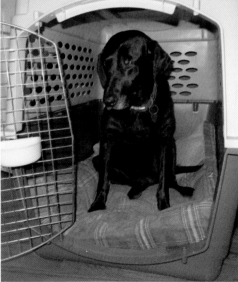

I would be so sad that I would go for days without eating, and my owner finally realized, as I already had, that my life was meant to be spent with Row. When he called Row and said I was no longer "his dog," she agreed, and for the last ten years she and I have been a team, and I have been the best dog she has ever had. Well, at least that's what Row, my mom, tells me.

When she introduces me now, she likes to say that I was a "rescue" dog — rescued from a life outdoors or in the back of a truck. But the truth is — I really rescued her. You see, the year before I met my mom, she was being treated for cancer. She had a couple of surgeries and then spent most

of the year going through chemotherapy and radiation. While she had many friends helping her, she was still without someone by her side day and night to help fill the void that only a loyal dog can do. I knew in my heart that we were meant to be together.

This book is about our story.
We hope you enjoy the journey.

From Hunting Dog to Frisbee Champion?

About the time Mom finished her cancer treatments, she realized that she needed to work less and take better care of herself so she became a part-time employee for her company. This also gave her more free time to spend with me.

We would go for long walks and do my favorite things, like going to the park where I could catch the frisbee. All she ever had to do was say the word *park* or *frisbee* and I'd be at the door ready to go. Mom thinks my vocabulary is limited to only a

few words because of how I react to them, but I understand a lot more words than she thinks. They're just not so exciting to me. Most of my dog friends feel the same.

Although I was no longer a duck-hunting dog, I was still a Labrador, and retrieving is built into our DNA. I like to retrieve anything: frisbee, ball, bumper, pinecone, and even a stick, if that's the only thing available. Humans find this behavior a bit obsessive, but for us Labs, it's totally normal.

I spent much of my "puphood" with a trainer, so at an early age I learned all the "good-dog" etiquette: *Sit — Stay — Heel.*

My trainer taught me not to be a barker and always to mind my owner. My mom says she doesn't know if these are characteristics of all Labradors because I'm her first one, but she does say that I'm the most well-trained and well-mannered dog she has ever had. I am so well trained that when we walk or play, I don't even need a leash because I'm always right by my mom. Unless I am retrieving something — then it's fetch and bring right back to her so she can throw it again, and again, and again.

In the first few years we were together, there wasn't a dog around that could out-fetch me. My mom and I would have

a contest at the park to see how many times I could catch the frisbee without missing. I'm not sure who was the most disappointed when I missed, but I can secretly tell you that when I missed, it was because Mom made a bad toss!

Now that I'm older, it's clear that the many years of frisbee playing have taken a toll on my joints. Like many other athletes, I'm paying the price for all that fun. My mom sometimes tells me that if she had it to do over, she would be more cautious about letting me run, jump, and fetch. But I tell her that I would not have had it any other way — even though it means some pain in my older life.

It was, and is, the thing (next to my mom) that I love most in life. My days of retrieving are pretty much behind me now and exist mostly in my dreams as my feet twitch in happy remembrance of those times gone by.

In the first few years with my mom, we traveled around the countryside and hiked in the mountains, and I really began to come into my own as a true traveling dog. My days as the duck dog in the back of the truck began to fade in my memory. Of course in my hunting days, I was a natural swimmer and loved to go jumping into any lake or stream I could find, but I had never been to the ocean.

Mom took me to visit friends who live at the beach, and we took their boat to a remote island to let me and my friend Sparky, a handsome Standard Poodle, swim in the ocean. We met up with some other friends and their sixteen-year-old daughter.

Now Sparky could care less about swimming — one of the big differences between Labs and Poodles. As for me, I found a willing frisbee-thrower in Mom's friend's daughter, who spent hours throwing the frisbee into the waves for me to fetch. I was having so much fun, I didn't realize that every time I grabbed the frisbee, I also took in some sea water.

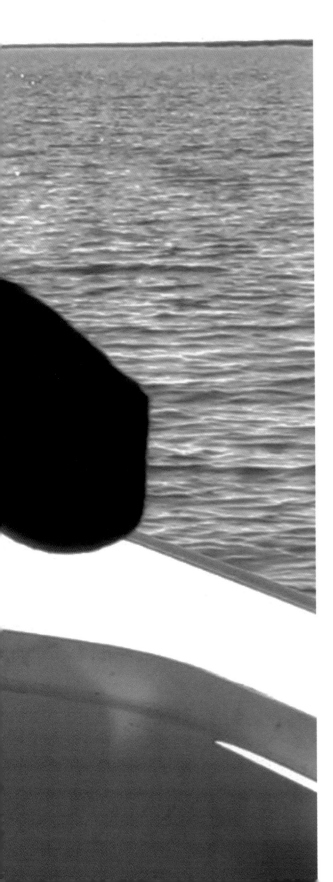

Boy, did I learn a valuable lesson. Let's just say that projectile at both ends was the price I paid for that day of fun. And my mom paid the price that night with no sleep.

Sea = Fun

Seawater = No Fun

Getting Ready *for* International Travel

After our amazing first few years together, Mom had a big treat for me. With our close friends Carol Ann and Bunny, she bought a house in the south of France. When they found the property, one of her first thoughts was, "Mac's going to love this place!" At least that's what she told me.

Though not sure what travel from the U.S. to France would entail, I'm always up for anything Mom wants me to do, and I never complain. She did lots of research on the best way to get me to France. 🐾²

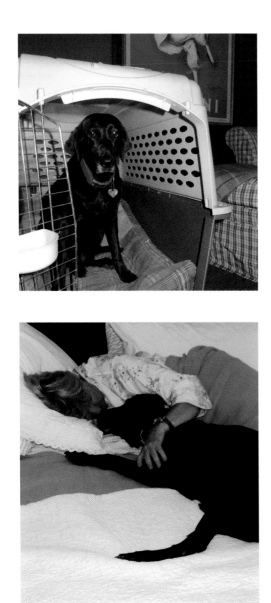

Mom explained that I'd have to travel in a kennel in the bottom of the airplane. Even though I had spent most of my youth in a kennel, I had not been in a cage for a number of years since then. So for the month before our first big trip, Mom put in her bedroom a travel kennel with my bed inside. In my bed she'd put one of my favorite toys, and just to make her happy, I'd sleep there every night.

In the past, I would sometimes sleep in the bed with her, though she has never liked to admit that. Now that I'm older and a bit less flexible, I'm not able to jump up on the bed, so we both cherish those past times when we were able to snuggle, even though my mom doesn't say this out loud.

Once they put me into the cargo section of the airplane, the baggage handlers inform the pilot and flight crew that I'm safely aboard, and they in turn inform my mom.🐾[3]

She has told me on many occasions that once she's seated, she tells the flight attendant that she must be sure I'm on the airplane, because if no one comes with the required copy of the label indicating that I'm on board, she will get off the plane. She says this

sometimes makes the flight attendants either laugh or frown — depending on how "dog friendly" they are. I know what she means by "dog friendly." Some of my dog friends are not so "people friendly" either.

In any event, after loading me into cargo, they've always come to tell Mom that I'm on the airplane. A few times, the pilot has personally checked on me and then come to tell her.

She believes that you can't be too careful when it comes to protecting your best friend. Didn't I tell you that my mom takes really good care of me?

Even when everything goes smoothly, it's still a little stressful. I remember the first time Mom watched them wheel me away and out of her view. I was sad and a little worried about where I was going, but I was mostly sad because I could see how watching me leave had made my mom very anxious.

I curl up, go to sleep, and wake up when I hear the airplane touch down. Once we arrive, I'm brought to a special baggage claim area for animals and oversized containers — for which I qualify on both counts. Though I wasn't uncomfortable in my kennel, that first flight was new and a bit scary because I wasn't sure what to expect.

Now that I am a seasoned traveler, I can tell you that most airports have an area where pets are allowed to "relieve themselves," but not all airports do. If you are traveling with your pet, you might want to check on this. I, luckily, can go for a long time without a bathroom break and have never had a problem.

I'm also a bit particular about where I go to the bathroom. Even though I'm usually ready for this relief, and my Mom encourages me, I refuse to go on the pavement. My paws will only allow me to use the bathroom if I am on dirt or preferably grass, and I mean real grass — none of that fake plastic grass. 🐾[4]

I may have painted a grim picture of this whole process, but I wanted you to understand what's involved and that these procedures don't pose impossible obstacles. Once you get to your final destination, it's worth the time and effort the preparation takes. I knew no matter what we'd go through together, Mom would never let anything happen to me.

My Arrival at Le Vivier, Our Home in the South of France

My mom had told me all about our new home in the south of France and how much I was going to like running and playing in the countryside. Our home even has a name: *Le Vivier,* which roughly translated means "the river that never runs dry." Though the French name didn't really impress me so much, I can tell you that I really loved having a river to play in so close to our house. But the river was just one of the awesome things about *Le Vivier.*

Our house is a big old farmhouse, almost nine hundred years old. That was hard to imagine as I had never seen anything that old in America. There were gardens and walkways and even a large open field, where — once my mom mowed and plowed it — would make for a great frisbee meadow. I even had my very own swimming pool. She was right — it was doggy heaven. My own pool to cool off in, my own river to swim in, and even my own frisbee field to fetch in. Paradise!

The people "we" bought the house from had not really been dog people, but they were very fond of cats. They adopted and found homes for many over the years. I

had never really been around cats, and Mom failed to tell me that she had made a deal with the previous owners of *Le Vivier* to take care of the six cats they were leaving behind. I didn't really want my mom to know, because I didn't want her to think of me as a wimpy dog, but I was actually afraid of these cats. Even though I was much bigger, it was clear that they had been residents of *Le Vivier* much longer than I so I'd have to get used to them — not the other way around.

Over time, we did get used to each other and even made friends. However, on more than one occasion, when I tried to get a little too friendly, I'd get a good

smack. I quickly learned my boundaries with the cats. One thing I know for sure: cats are more complicated than dogs.

Our country farmhouse is just outside a small village of about 1500 residents in the Languedoc region, near the Mediterranean and about an hour from the Spanish border. I know Mom really bought this house for me, but she also thought it would be a great place for friends and family to visit. Neither of us envisioned that over the first few years we would become a real part of the village and make lifelong friends (of both the human and animal variety) and that they would become a part of our lives forever.

We live in a very beautiful part of France. Perhaps not as visited as some other French regions, the Languedoc offers some wonderful attractions. A little known fact is that this region is the largest producer of wine in France. I know you're thinking that dogs really shouldn't drink wine — and I don't — but my mom has been known to raise a glass or two. We even have a vineyard on our property, where the grapes are harvested every October to go to the local wine "cooperative." Mom and I try to spend about six months a year at our French home 🐾[5] and have been able to see the harvest. Mom thinks it's interesting, but I stay out of the way of the big machines that pick the grapes.

Because we are so close to the Mediterranean, this region also has fantastic seafood and especially good local oysters. Now I don't care much for seafood, but when my mom roasts oysters in the outdoor fireplace, we always have to share some with the cats.

There is also another famous local dish, the cassoulet. While I may not like seafood, leftover cassoulet is another story. Yes, I have retrieved ducks in my past, but now I only savor the leftover duck confit that sits on top of Mom's cassoulet.

This dish was invented in a nearby town called Castelnaudary, which is halfway

between Carcassonne and Toulouse, also in the Languedoc region. Toulouse, the home of Airbus, is a beautiful city on the Garonne River. Carcassonne is the home of La Cité, the oldest, largest walled city in Europe. Mom and I have visited both cities often, and while I loved walking around La Cité, my mom and I now send our guests there on their own. You can be a tourist just so many times! At least that's what my mom tells me.

We are in a valley between the Black Mountains (*Montagne Noir*) and the Corbières, which are the foothills just north of the Pyrenees. In the first few years of living in this region, Mom and

I covered hundreds of miles hiking, where we discovered many beautiful hidden paths through the hills and vineyards. The Canal du Midi, built in the late 1600s, runs across the south of France and originally provided a way to ship goods from the Atlantic to the Mediterranean. Today it's primarily used by vacationers taking leisurely boat trips through the locks while visiting the many interesting villages along the way.

Mom and I love to take long walks down the paths on either side of the canal, and I've been known to take a swim or two as well as chase after an occasional duck — just for old times' sake. Sometimes we

take a picnic and watch the boaters work their boats through the locks.

One of the very best things about the south of France — or really Europe in general — is that they love their pets. Dogs are allowed pretty much everywhere, so when we take our long walks along the Canal du Midi or on the beaches of the Mediterranean and stop at restaurants along the way for a bite to eat, I've never been turned away. I've found this to be true throughout most of Europe, including some of its very best restaurants.

One time we were at a very beautiful outdoor café and needed an extra chair.

The table next to us had a lovely Miniature Poodle sitting in a chair, and Mom asked if we might use the chair. Reluctantly the owner moved her male dog to the ground. He proceeded to lift his leg and pee right on my mom's foot. She didn't think it was funny. Don't tell her, but I did.

Becoming a Service Dog

After the first few years of traveling back and forth between the United States and France, my mom began to have a problem with her blood pressure. With a heart condition from birth, she'd always seen a cardiologist annually, and when he asked her under which conditions her blood pressure became dangerously high, she indicated that it was when she had to place me in the baggage section of the airplane. He suggested that she have me trained as a service dog because it is a medical fact that simply petting an animal, or

59

being in the companionship of one, lowers your blood pressure by as much as thirty percent. Mom began to research this service-dog training. Because I had been trained as a hunting dog, I had already learned all forms of hand and voice commands; it did not take long for me to qualify for all of the service dog requirements. It was also essential that I displayed a calm disposition and did not bark or show aggression in public. Here my earlier training really paid off. These last hurdles may sound easy, but many dogs would find them impossible.

Mom spent lots of time training me so that I clearly understood the difference

between work and play. When I was in training, we would go to very busy places: malls, train stations, and airports, where I could not talk with anyone other than my mom. I don't know how I knew, but instinctively when my service dog vest was put on me, I became a true working dog. I would not even look at anyone else, and I listened and obeyed my mom's every command. We found that in addition to helping control her blood pressure, especially on the long flights to and from Europe, I am able to perform other service and therapy-dog duties.

My favorite is visiting nursing homes. It's amazing how much a visit from a dog like me can brighten the day for someone who's not had visitors for a while. We found that there are many ways that specially trained dogs can serve and assist. Most people immediately think of the amazing dogs trained to work with the deaf and the blind, but there are many other situations where dogs provide assistance.

Children who find it difficult to read aloud to people find reading to an animal much less intimidating. People with autism, epilepsy, depression, schizophrenia, post-traumatic stress disorder, bipolar disorder, and other psychological problems — to name just a few — have been shown to respond very well medically to the

assistance of a service/therapy animal. Aren't we working dogs great? At least that's what my mom tells me.

For Mom, it made a huge difference to her health. Because I was now able to travel in the airplane passenger cabin with her, her blood pressure became much more stable. I must say that mine has improved as well. We are very careful not to abuse my certification as a service dog, and I only wear my vest when I am working. I'm sure that not all dogs would so easily pass the requirements, but I'm not just any dog — my disposition, early intensive training, and general need to please made me a perfect candidate.

When we fly, I remain at Mom's feet during the flight and most people never even know that I am there. In the four years I have been a service dog, there has never been one incident or complaint. I'm so quiet that on a number of occasions when we arrived at our destination, I've heard someone say, "Did you know there was a dog sitting near us this whole flight? Just wish our kids were that well behaved." My tail wags because I know my mom is proud.

Traveling in France,
Inside and Outside
of the Languedoc Region

Mom and I spent the first few years exploring our area: the Minervois district in the Languedoc region, where there is much to see and do. We began by taking day trips. We visited Albi, famous for the Sainte Cécile Cathedral, where the rise of the Cathars and subsequent takeover by the Catholic Church occurred. The home of the Toulouse-Lautrec museum, Albi sits on the picturesque River Tarn, across which spans the beautiful Millau

Bridge. While I wasn't allowed in the cathedral or the museum, I had fun hanging outside with Mom's friends while they took turns touring.

Another favorite day trip was to Roquefort, where the delicious blue cheese comes from. I didn't get to go into the cheese caves, but enjoyed bites of Mom's blue cheese after her lunch. When I first sniffed the cheese, I found it smelled terrible and couldn't imagine why humans would want to eat that. But boy did it taste good. I guess it's just one more difference between dogs and humans. I couldn't make fun of Mom for eating something that smells bad because she never makes fun of me for sniffing other dogs' bottoms.

Of course we've had many day trips to other interesting and famous places. Another favorite of ours is Collioure, a picturesque beach town just north of the Spanish border and south of Perpignan. Here I can not only sit with Mom and her friends at the quaint outdoor restaurants, but, weather permitting, I can take a swim in the Mediterranean! When you are in this part of France, you will also want to visit Banyuls for their wonderful dessert wine. Mom tells me it is medicinal, but I know better.

Just across the French border in Spain is another great village called Cadaqués, a beautiful coastal town with excellent restaurants and beaches. There you can visit the home where Salvadore Dalí, the artist, was born. When heading back north towards our home, we sometimes stop in Perpignan, a much larger city with wonderful museums, cathedrals, and even a palace where the French kings lived between the 12th and 14th centuries. The palace's gorgeous gardens make it well worth a visit.

Other short day trips include Lagrasse, a village that most guidebooks say is one of the most beautiful small villages in France; Mirepoix, a quaint 13th-century

village with a wonderful central market, and Limoux, where they have a Mardi Gras celebration and lots of great wine. I was even allowed into the winery in Limoux, where the champagne method of winemaking was invented a hundred years before it was named in the northern part of the country. One of my favorite villages is Minerve, perched atop a large gorge and best known as one of the last strongholds of the Cathars.

Also close by are the famous underground Cabrespine caves and the Cathar castle ruins of Lastours, with amazing views. As we began to explore more that the south of France had to offer, we began to take longer overnight trips.

One of my favorite trips was with our friend Robin to the Carmargue, north of Arles, between the Mediterranean and the mouth of the Rhône River. The Camargue regional park lies in the Provence region, just to the east of the Languedoc. Most famous for the beautiful white horses that once ran wild on the beaches, the Camargue is also known for its bulls. We went to the Bull Festival where the French cowboys ride the beautiful horses to herd the bulls to the marsh. It was quite spectacular, but I took great care to stay out of the way of both the horses and the bulls at the festival, but I got to visit with the horses at our hotel.

The Carmargue has another special attraction: the pink flamingos that flock to the ocean marsh by the thousands. I kept away from them, too.

When you travel to the Carmargue, you should also visit nearby Arles, Saint Rémy, and Nîmes. We took side trips to Arles with its beautiful Roman arena in the center of town. Arles is also the home of one of Mom's favorite bands, the Gypsy Kings. A beautiful town, where Van Gogh painted *Starry Night*, Saint Rémy has one of the very best weekly markets with not only the freshest of produce, meats, and seafood, but also virtually every gift item you might want to purchase

for friends back home. They also have a wonderful chocolate shop — okay for humans but not so healthy for dogs. At least that's what my mom tells me. I tell her it probably isn't good for her either, but she just ignores me.

Just across the border of Provence, we visited Nîmes, where we toured the fascinating Roman amphitheater, and I could only imagine what might have occurred there hundreds of years before with animals much larger than me. I'm sure I could smell traces of lions and tigers, but maybe it was only the local stray cats. Either way, I could sniff out no evidence that dogs had ever fetched frisbees here.

Mom had a visitor who needed to go to Marseille for work, so I was invited to travel with them for another great outing. Most people don't realize that Marseille is the second largest city in France — just behind Paris. We stayed near the port, where you will find an abundance of hotels and restaurants to pick from — many dog friendly. One day we took a boat to one of the remote islands where we could have lunch and I could swim. It was one of my most favorite days as Mom threw the stick so many times for me that I slept all the way back to the port.

The next day, we took a long walk through the city to the top of the hill and the

cathedral Notre-Dame de la Garde (our Lady of the Guard), where we had amazing views of the city and the Mediterranean. I was not allowed to go in, but Mom and our friend Stacy took turns outside with me so they could each visit. The walk downhill was easier, but I had to use my nose to help them find their way back to the hotel. Mom and Stacy kept pulling out the map when all they really had to do was follow me.

One of the famous dishes in Marseille is bouillabaisse — a type of broth filled with seafood and vegetables. Mom and Stacy liked it — but no seafood for me. However, I did get to have a bite of wonderful French bread dipped into the broth. Yum!

Mom has a good college friend who lives with her husband in the English countryside. I've not been allowed to go to England yet, as the laws have been very strict about dogs crossing the border, but the laws are changing, and I hope to go there some day. These same friends also have a home in France that I did get to visit. Their cottage is in a small village in the center of France, near Bourges.

Mom's friend Robbie and her husband took us to visit one of their neighbors, a yellow Labrador named Albion. He and I played ball and romped in his beautiful garden. He made me realize that I was no longer a puppy but a mature lady.

I am so happy that over the years in France, Mom and I have not only hosted many of our friends and family for visits to *Le Vivier*, we have met so many wonderful people who continue to invite us into their homes. One of our favorite places to visit is the home of our friends Michele and Greg. Originally from Australia, they are now retired and share their time between Florida and the south of France. Their home is on the other side of France from us, but only about a three-hour drive, so we try and go as often as possible. The first time Mom and I visited them, they weren't sure about having a dog in the house. Not only do they have a beautiful château, they also have chickens and parrots.

Mom assured them that I would have no interest in either, and our first visit went so well that now they invite Mom to visit only if she brings me!

Michele and Greg live in a wonderful village about a mile from Saint-Émilion. This region — Bordeaux — doesn't grow as many grapes as our region, but Mom tells me that people who buy the wine from this region pay a lot more for it. Of course, because Bordeaux is so famous for its wine, Mom and her friends love to taste the wine from the area, but I stay with the chickens and parrots at the beautiful château, since wine isn't on my menu.

Another famous wine region, north of the Languedoc, is Burgundy.🐾[6] While Mom has been there many times, I made my first trip there last year and was allowed to go everywhere the humans went. We stayed in the village of Igé at the Château Igé, where I had fantastic gardens to run around in and was allowed to sit with Mom during meals. I also got to go into the village of Mâcon into the wineries and tourist center.

The biggest problem when we travel to the various wine regions is that Mom likes wine. So she buys wine to take home. By the time the car is loaded, I barely have any room to get on my bed.

When Mom was younger, she lived in Paris on assignment for her company. She has told me many times how much I would love that very beautiful and dog-friendly city, so last year she took me there. We took the train 🐾[7] from Narbonne to Paris and spent a week with our friend Sandy and our friend Sue at her fabulous Paris apartment.

Sue lives in the 7th Arrondissement, the same area my mom had lived in, so Mom knew all the wonderful parks where I could walk and play. We spent days just walking and looking and reminiscing in one of the most beautiful cities in the world.

Mom even bought me a new red leather collar, and I'm feeling very stylish these days. All my dog friends envy my beautiful Parisian collar. I overheard Mom tell someone that she paid more for my collar than she would have spent on a belt for herself. Didn't I tell you my mom is really good to me?

My Travels Outside of France

In the United States, my travel has been limited simply by the vast size of our country, but the great thing about Europe, I just jump in the car, take a long nap, and the next thing I know, my mom has me safely across the border into another country.

Because we fly in and out of Barcelona, we've spent lots of time there. It's a wonderful place to walk, eat, and shop. Barcelona also has some wonderful dog-friendly hotels.

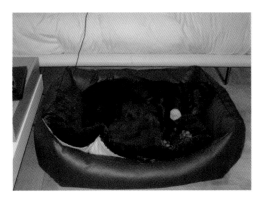

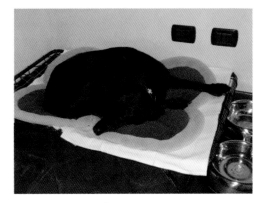

We stayed one time at the Mandarin Oriental Hotel right in the middle of Barcelona. When Mom called to make the reservation and asked if they allowed dogs, the sales manager said, "The only problem with dogs staying here is that they never want to leave." And he was right. When we got to the room, we found a large leather dog bed, raised food and water bowls, and dog treats. Now that is luxury. I don't mention this experience to my dog friends; they would be very jealous.

If we have an early flight, sometimes we stay at an airport hotel where they have a shuttle that takes Mom and me to the airport. Though they are also pet friendly and provide a bed, I have to say it isn't like the leather one at the Mandarin Oriental Hotel. I've also stayed at the Ritz Carlton and the W Hotel, both of which are on the water and dog friendly.

I love staying in Barcelona because I can swim in the beautiful Mediterranean. It's funny, but now that I know my way around most of southern Europe, the Mediterranean smells different in France, Spain, and Italy. I can't tell if it's because of the type of fish or the type of people swimming there.

Sometimes on our way from southern France to Spain, we spend the night in

Girona, a wonderful city that sits in the foothills of the Pyrenees about half way between the French/Spanish border and Barcelona. A city of many bridges since four different rivers converge here, the two halves of the city are connected by these bridges. There is so much to see and do here with another batch of wonderful restaurants to try.

Mom doesn't let me eat food from the table or I would be in big trouble. I know that for me to continue going to these wonderful places, especially restaurants, I must be really well behaved, so I just crawl under the table and act like I'm invisible. When we leave, my reward comes when

someone says, "What a good dog!" My tail wags and that's the same as a human smile.

Some of our other favorite places in Spain are on the opposite side of the country but also on the water – the Atlantic Ocean. We've been to San Sebastián a number of times and find that the Hotel Maria Christina, with lots of parks nearby, is very accommodating for pets. Did I say that the hotel is also near the beach?

Usually, when we drive to San Sebastián, we go back up into France to visit our friends in Bordeaux, so we almost always have to make a stop on the way at the beautiful village of Saint-Jean-de-Luz, just over the Spanish border, back in France. Next we usually head up to Biarritz, which has some of the best surfing in the world. I've never mastered the art of surfing, but I know if I put my mind to it, I would be really good. Since Mom can't surf and therefore can't teach me, we have to be content taking a swim in the ocean. This part of northern Spain and southern France is known as the Basque Region and has some amazing restaurants. I know, because Mom occasionally gets me a "doggy" bag to take home.

Every couple of years, Mom's Australian friends, who first introduced her to the Languedoc region, organize a wine-

tasting trip to a location in a different part of Europe. A few years ago, they asked my mom to go, but she said she didn't feel good leaving me behind. Since most of the group had met me and knew I was well behaved, they checked to see if I could stay at the villa they were renting in Tuscany and if I might even be allowed to attend some of the planned events. Luckily, Italy is a very dog-friendly country, too, so I made my first trip to Italy.

Mom took our friend Stacy, and we decided to make a few stops on the way. We drove along the Mediterranean, and our first stay was in Santa Margherita at the wonderful Hotel Continental.

My room had a big balcony where I could watch the ocean while Mom and Stacy visited. We drove to Portofino for dinner, and I got to view all the "beautiful people" while we ate at a sidewalk café. I didn't see many other dogs, but I sure did get a lot of pats on the head from all the "beautiful people" we saw strolling around.

I later found out that the reason I didn't see many dogs is that there isn't much dirt or grass in Portofino — just lots of water, boats, stone, and cement. So for us four-legged animals looking for a bathroom, best to stay around the corner in Santa Margherita.

We spent a week in a villa just outside of Chianti in the lovely countryside of Tuscany. I loved being in the country, and not only did the villa's owners allow dogs, they also had a dog-friendly swimming pool where I could cool off after a long day of waiting while Mom and her friends tasted the best of Tuscany's wines. The owner had a Jack Russell Terrier that I made friends with, and we spent time together outside while Mom and her friends took a cooking class inside the kitchen. I fogged up the window of the door looking in at them while they cooked some amazing Italian food and I wondered why I had to remain outside.

On the way back to the Languedoc, we stopped in Parma — famous for ham and Parmesan cheese, two of my favorite foods. All the way home, I could smell the ham and cheese Mom had bought to take back to France. It was all wrapped up right next to me in the car. Pure torture!

Last year with our friend Sandy, Mom and I took a trip back to Italy to Lake Como. We stayed in Bellagio at the Grand Hotel Villa Serbelloni. This majestic hotel even had for the door of our room a special tag that read, "Pet Inside." What a great way to prevent the maid being shocked when she entered and saw me.

The gardens around this hotel are spectacular, and Mom took me for lots of long walks every day. There was even a beach where I could take my daily swim. Sometimes Mom swam with me. Didn't I tell you I was a lucky girl?

Trials and Tribulations for a Dog in the Country

While my life in the south of France has been a dog's dream, there have also been a few nightmares that I should share with you so that your four-legged friends can avoid them.

Fetching was something I loved so much, I didn't know when to tell my mom to stop throwing because I never wanted to stop playing. All that exercise finally resulted in a torn ligament in my back leg. The veterinarians refer to this as cranial

cruciate ligament tear, while humans refer to it as ACL: anterior cruciate ligament tear. In many cases, this happens to athletes of both the animal and human kind. While many veterinarians in France perform this surgery, the recovery time takes about six months, so Mom decided she would keep me quiet and comfortable until we could get back to the U.S. for the surgery. It was a long and painful recovery, mostly because I couldn't run and play, but in six months, I was almost as good as new.

My other main trauma in the south of France has to do with the seeds (diaspore) at the top of the wild grasses that grow

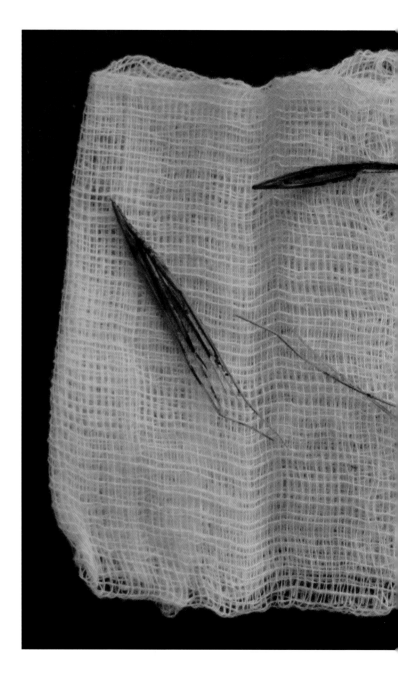

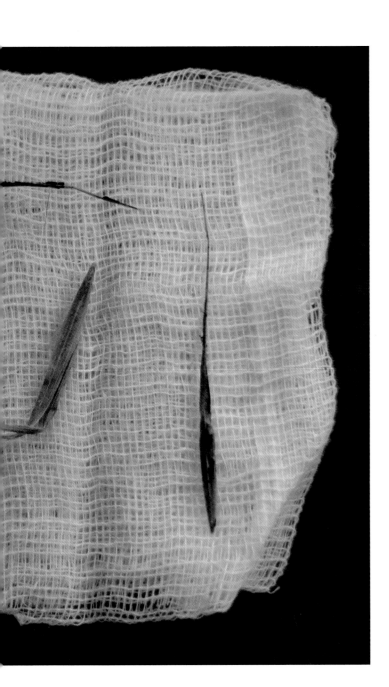

abundantly in the countryside there. Sometimes these grasses are referred to as "foxtails" because they resemble the stubble in the tail of a fox. You humans know them as the difficult-to-remove grass seeds that stick to your socks when you walk in fields. In animals, they like to lodge themselves in our noses, ears, eyes, or any orifice! Once in, they can only move forward, and this is where the problem lies. They love my nose and have managed to insert themselves there on quite a few occasions.

The first time, I kept sneezing, thinking this would dislodge the spore, but it only forced it deeper. As the spore entered my lungs, the sneeze turned into a cough, and Mom became very worried. She took me to the local vet, who immediately recognized the problem and sent me to the nearest veterinary surgeon. With an endoscope he was able to find and remove the dangerous grass seeds while I was anesthetized. He explained to my mom that had they gone any further into my bronchial tubes, they could have gone to my heart and killed me. I didn't really worry about any of that, but I sure was glad when I could stop trying to cough those stupid things out.

I don't know why, but these grass seeds have lodged themselves in my nose a number of times. Luckily, after that first scare, Mom

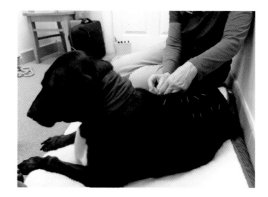

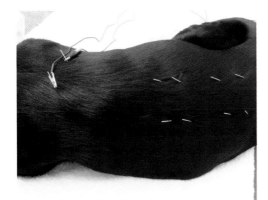

knew what to do and would haul me to the vet every time it happened.

Once, as we waited our turn at the vet's office, a handsome Dachshund was also waiting. His owner said that the same thing happened to him, but instead of his nose, the seed went into his penis. Now I don't have one of those, but can only imagine how painful that would be! Lesson learned: beware of the grass seeds![8]

As I've grown older, like most dogs, especially athletic ones like me, my joints have also aged and I'm not able to do all the things my mind thinks I can do. Mom says this is happening to her as well.

To help me stay as mobile as possible, Mom takes me to a veterinarian that specializes in both traditional and non-traditional medicine. She performs acupuncture on me when my joints get especially sore, and this helps with the pain. This vet also does laser therapy for my arthritis. Did I tell you that my mom takes really good care of me?

Mac and Friends

I am so fortunate in so many ways,
but I'm particularly lucky in the many
friends I've made all over the world.

Some come to visit us.

Some we go to visit.

Some have four legs. Some have two.

Some are human. Some are not.

Some are dogs. Some are not.

And some are not even real.

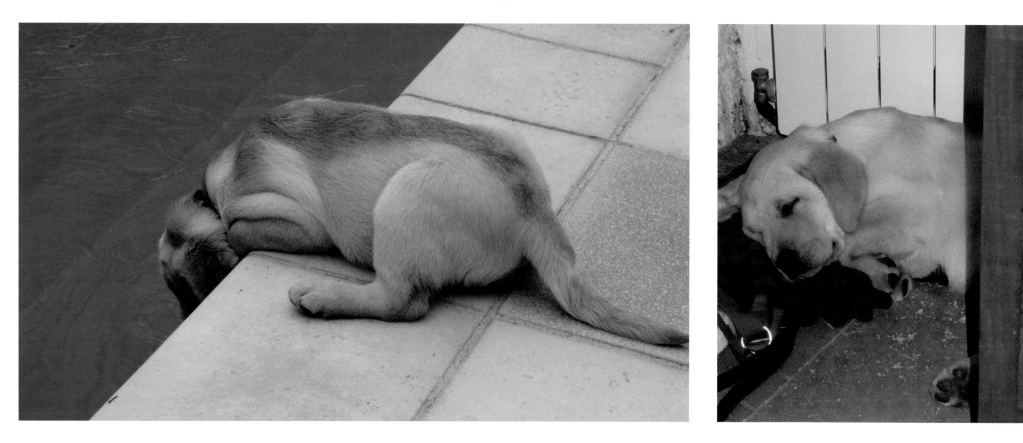

My Message

I wrote this book to share my wonderful life with other dogs and dog lovers. I wanted to show that a dog can rescue a human just as well as a human can rescue a dog, and when the two come together, it's a beautiful thing. Our life together has been better than either of us imagined it alone. We hope you enjoyed our story and the pictures that help tell it, but the real reason is so that you will recommend our book to others. One hundred percent of our profits from this book will go to animal rescue to make sure that other animals might live the life that we have.

Dog bless you and God bless you for reading our book.

Mac

And since I wasn't able to hold a pen in my paw or type on the computer keyboard, my faithful transcriber and my mom…

Row

Paw Notes

Paw notes are like footnotes, except from my paw since I don't have a foot. I've included additional details to help clarify certain sections in the book.

1 One of the most popular breeds, the Labrador Retriever dog was first bred in Canada, and today there are two unofficial types of Labrador Retrievers — the American Labrador and the English Labrador. The American Labrador is taller, leaner with a longer and thinner head, while the English Labrador is shorter and stockier with a larger head. My cousin the English Lab and I are both wonderful dogs.

2 Some airlines do not allow pets of any kind to be checked or carried onto an airplane. On other airlines, pets over a certain weight are not allowed in the cabin of the airplane at all unless they are certified service or therapy dogs. I found this quite interesting, since I know for a fact that I'm better behaved than some of my mom's friends that travel with her. In any event, she found that Delta Airlines did indeed, for a fee, allow dogs to travel in the cargo

section of the airplane. She also researched all the specific requirements for travel to a different country. There were very specific details for the kind and size of kennel that I would have to travel in. Not only did it have to be a certain size, but it also had to allow a certain amount of room above my head when I sat. A container for food and water had to be attached to the crate, and a supply of food and water had to be provided — just in case there were delays with travel so I could be given food and water if need be. Luckily that never happened to me.

In addition, a lot of paperwork had to be prepared. Before every trip, my Mom would take me to the veterinarian to get a health certificate. This would confirm to the "authorities" that I was in good health to travel and that all my shots were current. In addition, I had to have a certain type of chip put into my skin to track me if something should happen to me during this process. Of course, I'd never try to "escape," but it has happened in the past that dogs got out of their kennels somehow and were never seen again. This made the airlines nervous, and would have made my mom nervous, but she knew that I would never run away.

In addition to the health certificate prepared by an authorized veterinarian, the health certificate then had to be stamped and approved by the State Veterinarian, who is part of the U.S. Department of Agriculture. This had to be done within 10 days of travel. The required health certificate had to be specific for the country we were going to and in the language of that country.

So that I would not have to change airplanes, we flew to the closest direct international airport to our home in the south of France, which is Barcelona, Spain, so our documents were in Spanish even though we would cross the border to our home in France. One good thing for dogs traveling within the European Union is that there are no border patrol stations any more to travel between one country and the other, but, just in case, my mom got a passport for me.

In the past some European countries have required pets to go into quarantine, even with proper documents, but this is no longer much of an issue. I'm a very good dog, but even I would not have liked to do this. Who could know that immigration laws for dogs are just as complicated as they are for humans?

🐾 3   On the day of my first international trip, I could see that my mom was a little anxious. The airline's instructions for traveling with pets suggest that we arrive three hours before the flight. I don't wear a watch myself; time isn't as important to me as it is to Mom. We checked in at the special counter for people traveling with pets, where they inspected my paperwork and kennel, and read the identification chip in my neck.

🐾 4   Mom gives me food and water the night before we fly and makes sure I have lots of opportunity to "do my business" before we go into the airport. She gives me a little water before we fly, but doesn't give me any food until we get to our destination. I'm a little hungry when I arrive, but this makes the trip easier for both of us.

The airline is required to place a label on my kennel indicating my name, my mom's name, the flight number, and my mom's seat number. Because the airline is supposed to board animals last into a special area of baggage, we sometimes have to sit on the tarmac a bit. Therefore, most airlines also restrict the time of year that we can travel so that we aren't outside in really hot or really cold weather for too long, just in case the flight is delayed.

🐾 5   If you are considering buying a home in another country, be sure to check carefully all the regulations first, including the tax implications and the number of consecutive months you can reside there.

🐾 6   The wine regions of France are historical regions and not the same as the modern geographical regions of France.

🐾 7   Many regional trains do not allow animals to travel, but the major trains, like the French TGV, do for a fee allow pets to travel with their owners. The cost is usually about one half that of an adult.

🐾 8   My vet in France tells me that I am an exception to the rule. While it is common for dogs to have these spores enter their noses, it almost never happens to a dog more than once in a dog-life. Guess I'm a slow learner!

Acknowledgements

I first started thinking of doing a book about my travels with Mac over a year ago. On occasion, during a trip here or there, I'd post a picture on Facebook of Mac in some wonderful location and would be inundated with comments back from friends saying that they wished they had the life that Mac has had and that she was better traveled than most people. Late last year, I began to plan my retirement and thought that as Mac is also reaching her own "retirement" age, it would be nice to pay a tribute to her for all she has done to make my life better.

While I've written a few books related to the work I've been involved in for over 40 years, human resources technology, I've never written anything more dear to my heart than this story of my best friend, Mackenzie. I retired in April and began to work diligently on turning Mac's story into this beautiful book. Also in April, Mac and I returned to France, where I completed the text and started to compile the thousands of photos I've taken over the years, pictures that might complement our story as the two of us have traveled the world.

My most diligent supporter and contributor is my good friend, college roommate, and editor, Robbie Butler-White. She has spent countless hours and late nights reviewing, editing, and refining Mac's story. A published writer, Robbie has been a dear friend for over 40 years, and her assistance on this project has been invaluable.

Another of my college roommates, Ann Ford Nermoe, also helped tremendously with her amazing photographs that complemented my own, especially the frisbee-dog action shots!

Picture editor Gibbs Hasty, who I've known since elementary school, helped take an amateur photographer's pictures and made them book quality. Thank you, Gibbs!

Tuck Tucker, President of Tucker-Castleberry Printing has kindly offered to let me store my books at his warehouse and given great advice about printing and shipping as this has been all new to me. I've also known Tuck since college.

Daniel Devlin, the only newcomer to my acknowledgements list, was introduced to me by Robbie and has been the guy to pull it all together in his gift of book design. You were the sanity that kept me and Robbie going.

Special thanks to David Richards, Caunes-Minervois photographer extraordinaire for my front cover, and art student Harvin Alert, my good friend Agu's son, who, while visiting our village, took the amazing portrait that now appears on the back cover of this book.

Dozens of my friends and family have been subjected to my reading sections aloud to them, asking for their input and reviews, borrowing pictures from their times with me and Mac, and generally driving them all crazy talking about this book. It has truly been a labor of love and while I can't name everyone — you know who you are and I love you for helping to make this a reality.

And, of course, I thank Mac for being the best dog I've ever had.

Row

Le Vivier, August 2013